The L███████'s
spo███████

by Roger Knights

It was the Lettermen's sports day. They all got up very early to practise their races.

sports

park

When they were ready, they hurried to the park where the sports day was being held. No one wanted to miss the first race.

Some of the Lettermen went in for the running race.

Ready, steady, go!

g o

They ran as fast as they could. They were all quite out of breath when they reached the end.

run

Next, the Lettermen
had to see how high
they could jump.
They took a huge
run-up and leaped
over the bar.

long

After that, they tried the long jump. Some Lettermen jumped such a long way and were really pleased that they had soft sand to land in.

Then came the egg
and spoon race.

The Lettermen
had to be extra
careful...

egg

spoon

...they were using real eggs!

Oh no! As they reached the winning post, some Lettermen dropped their eggs. That was the end of the race for them!

drop

The Letterman who went the slowest came up from behind and won the race because he had been so careful.

Perhaps they'll have better luck in the sack race. Remember, feet in the corners and jump!

sack

It wasn't as easy as the Lettermen thought, and soon almost all of them fell over.

fall

drink

By now, all the Lettermen
were out of breath and
they were very thirsty.

Then it was time for the relay race. Each Letterman ran for a part of the race, then passed the baton on.

relay

win

The team who ran the fastest won first prize. They were very pleased with themselves.

Not all the Lettermen could win first prize.
The ones that came last were very disappointed.

lose

In the end,
everyone
was given
a prize at
the Lettermen's
sports day.

It wasn't a very
big prize...

prize

...but it was what
Lettermen like best!